BIENVENUE EN FRANCE*

*Welcome to France

You can start exploring France with this great book of games. With each page turned, discover the country's specialities and curiosities in a fun way!

Ready for an exciting journey?
Let's go!

To make reading easier for you, difficult words have been highlighted in pink, and are explained in the glossary p.59.

THE MAP OF FRANCE
AND ITS REGIONS

Here is the map of France. As you can see, our country is divided
into thirteen large regions. From East to West and North to South,
they are all very different. Each has its own secrets, colours and landscapes.
Some even have their own language, like Brittany, Alsace or Corsica.
Such a change of scenery!

BONJOUR ! Hello!

My name is Romane and I'm 11 years old. Behind me is my brother, Jules, he's 9. We were both born in Tours, which is a lovely French town.
Can you see the half-timbered houses Jules is looking at?
They are typical in the old part of Tours.
But there are so many other places to discover in France.
Let's begin with the Loire Valley *châteaux*, right near here.

THE LOIRE VALLEY
CHÂTEAUX

1418. The Hundred Years' War. France and England were fighting. That year, the English were occupying Paris. The future King Charles VII (he was only 14 years old) had to flee the capital. **He found refuge in the lands surrounding the Loire River, that offered** good protection against the enemy

Peace returned in 1453, but **Charles VII enjoyed living in this area, and decided to call it home. As did his successors.** Right up until the arrival of Henry IV, many kings grew up or ruled near the Loire River.

Thanks to them, the region was endowed with sumptuous *châteaux*, mostly of Renaissance style. **The most famous among them?** Amboise, Chambord, Chenonceau, Villandry or even Azay-le-Rideau.

GAME

Find the 7 differences in the water's reflection of Chenonceau.

THE RENAISSANCE
(FROM THE LATE 15ᵀᴴ TO EARLY 17ᵀᴴ CENTURY)

At the time, French kings were waging a war against Italy. That is where they made the most incredible discovery: **Renaissance art.** This form of art could be found in literature, painting and architecture.
King Francis I fell in love with this new style. He even had the most famous Italian artist **come over to France: Leonardo da Vinci** (does the *Mona Lisa* ring a bell?).

The Renaissance era **marked the end of gloomy fortified castles.** People started drawing their inspiration from Italian palaces. Paler stone was used, the walls were adorned with mouldings, galleries were built to walk down, large windows were fitted to let the light in and magnificent staircases were created. **As for the gardens, they were as decorative as they were welcoming.**
        Such wonderful treasures!

Villandry's gardens

Follow the code to bring some colour to these Renaissance gardens.

A
B
C
D
E
F

JOURNEY THROUGH NANTES

As the sixth largest town in France, Nantes has a rich past: from **Jules Verne** (a very famous writer born in Nantes) to the city's old port and *château*. Nantes loves to re-invent its own past.

The best example? **The *"Machines de l'Île"*.** Built on the city's small island, these machines are in fact huge mechanical sculptures that now populate the island, which used to be a shipyard. When in Nantes, do not be surprised if you see visitors riding on a wood and iron elephant. It is 40 feet high!

GAME

In his many stories, Jules Verne imagined lots of fantastic machines. Get some ideas from these drawings and create your very own travelling machine.

HEADING TOWARDS THE ATLANTIC

Not far from Nantes lies the Atlantic coastline.
It can be wild, rocky or sandy, and is a prime place
for the summer holidays.

This is where **the vastest beaches in France are:**
La Baule (the longest in Europe!)
and Les Sables d'Olonne.

When you think Ocean, you also think islands.
Yeu and **Noirmoutier** are both heavens on Earth.
The Old Castle on the island of Yeu is really a must-see.
People say it may have inspired Hergé, the famous author of Tintin,
when writing *The Black Island*.

Atlantic ocean

THE ROUND-THE-WORLD TRIP STARTS HERE!

The **Vendée Globe** starts and finishes
here, in Les Sables d'Olonne:
it is an incredible round-the-world
boat race, where skippers sail alone,
without stopping
and with no assistance.

GAME To find out what the Vendée
Globe record is, add up
the numbers on the boats
of the same colour.

RECORD TO BEAT:

 DAYS   HOURS   MINUTES   SECONDS

9

SEA, SEA, SEA

Travelling further North, Brittany soon comes into view. This region is surrounded by the sea. A large variety of marine animals can be discovered there. Lots of birds such as gulls, Atlantic puffins, little egrets and Northern gannets enjoy living in this region.

Off the coast of Perros-Guirec, there is a wonderful ornithological reserve: the Seven Islands archipelago. It counts 181 bird species! Grey seals also love their company. Great encounters on the horizon!

cormorant

Northern gannet

puffin

Which of these 3 birds will collect the most fish? Draw a vertical line to find out.

cormorant

Northern gannet

puffin

The landscapes are spectacular here. Especially along the coast. It becomes pink near Trébeurden and grows wilder around Quiberon and Ouessant island. A little further South is a true gem: **the Morbihan Gulf.**
It is no doubt one of the most beautiful bays in the world. This small stretch of sea is in fact a gulf, which means a part of the sea spread inland.

Then, obviously, we have the islands. There are dozens of them. Little heavens on Earth. It feels almost like the Indian Ocean when on the Glénans islands. On Ouessant and Molène, it is as if you had reached the end of the world. The largest and perhaps the most beautiful was perfectly-named: Belle-Île ("Beautiful Island" in French).
You cannot say this did not make you want to come to Brittany.

GAME

```
C B R E H A T O G
I U E E N M E R L
D I L E X I O S E
E E S C B A R G N
O L S E A T Z H A
H L E Z T A U O N
B E I E M B R E N
  T N E N E L O M
```

BATZ
BELLE-ÎLE EN MER
BRÉHAT
CÉZEMBRE
GLÉNAN
GROIX
HOËDIC
HOUAT
SEIN
MOLÈNE

Find the names of these Breton islands in the grid. Any directions are possible. The remaining letters will give you the name of the island most towards to East.

THE LAND OF CRÊPES

If you come to Brittany, you will no doubt taste some *crêpes* (French pancakes). You can find them pretty much anywhere. Actually, there are two kinds: those made with wheat flour (which is tender) and those made with buckwheat (which is darker). Generally, wheat flour *crêpes* are eaten with sweet toppings, and the buckwheat ones are savoury. The latter are sometimes called *galettes*. The most common savoury crêpe is the "Complete": ham, egg and cheese. Yummy!

GAME *How many complete* **crêpes** *do you think we can make with the remaining ingredients?*

1 egg

2 pieces of cheese

and 1 slice of ham

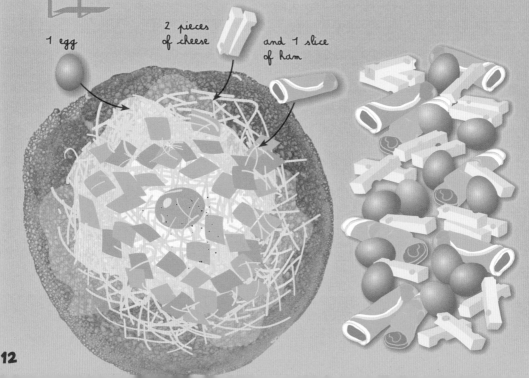

THE MYSTERY
OF THE RAISED STONES

Carnac,
a must-do.
We are now in the Bay
of Quiberon, just a few steps away
from the Morbihan Gulf. **This area
is known all over the world for its stones:
close to 3,000 menhirs are aligned over
2.5 miles!** The largest among them
is almost 20 feet tall.

GAME *Carry on the logical sequence
through the megaliths without
moving diagonally.*

**They say these megaliths were
set up between 5,000 and
3,000 years B.C. Their role is
still a mystery...** Many
hypotheses have tried
to explain these alignments.
They may have been religious
monuments to celebrate
the dead, or a huge
observatory used to measure
the position of the stars.
Such a puzzle...

*What wouldn't we do
to amuse our kids,
hey...*

A MARVELLOUS MOUNT

Picture a gigantic granite rock surrounded by water and shifting sands. Right at the top stands a proud and majestic abbey, whose construction began in the 11th century.

Welcome to the **Mont-Saint-Michel**, in Normandy. It is one of the most visited monuments in France. And it deserves that title. It can now be accessed by a bridge, but be careful, during high tides when the sea is all the way up, the Mont-Saint-Michel becomes an island.

In 966, monks settled down there and the town quickly started to attract many pilgrims.
A large church and houses were then built to welcome them.

What about Saint-Michel, I hear you ask?
The legend says that in 708, bishop Aubert built an initial church here upon request from archangel Michael. His statue stands on the spire at the top of the abbey.

GAME

Your turn to calculate how high the statue of archangel Michael stands above the Bay.

Way up there !

_____ ft

+112

_____

×2

__ +40

__

×2

___

×10

8

The Mont-Saint-Michel is classified as a Unesco World Heritage site.

6 JUNE 1944:
LANDINGS
IN NORMANDY

They are also known as _D Day_. At dawn on 6 June 1944, 140,000 Allied Force soldiers (**American** 🇺🇸, **Canadian** 🇨🇦 and **British** 🇬🇧) landed on Normandy's coastline. Their mission? To free France, occupied by the Germans since 1940. **This happened during World War II (1939-1945).**

This attack was given a code name: **operation _Overlord_.** Prepared in complete secrecy, it surprised the Germans who expected to see the Allied Forces arrive in the North of France, nearest to England.
The landing operation took place on five of Normandy's beaches, spread out over 50 miles. It was a decisive operation. After a harsh battle in Normandy, where thousands of people unfortunately died, **the city of Paris was freed on 25 August 1944.**

© caen memorial museum/S. Colomyès

Today, right near the beaches, in Caen or at the Memorial, you can relive this legendary operation by watching films, looking at war equipment and learning about historical events.

NORMANDY

*Sword *Juno *Gold *Omaha *Utah

* The five landing beaches

PARADISE
FOR IMPRESSIONISTS

In the second half of the 19th century,
a new pictorial movement began
in France: **impressionism.**
Rather than representing precise reality,
impressionists preferred to paint their impressions.
They expressed themselves using small touches of colour. They also loved
to work outdoors, with a lovely landscape before them. With the sea nearby
and its ever-changing light, Normandy became a true open-sky workshop
for this form of art. The most famous artists came to rest their easel
in this region: Renoir, Courbet, Pissarro and Eugène Boudin.
The latter influenced the most famous of them all: Claude Monet.

GAME

*In 1883, Claude Monet settled down in Giverny - a little village in Normandy.
He painted there until he passed away in 1926. His house can now be
visited, as can his garden where he did a famous series of paintings.*

*To find out the name of these paintings, take a
close look at the garden, the letters are hidden
there. The colour code will tell you where to look.*

Museum of modern art "André Malraux Le Havre"

FROM
TO
CHEESE

Cows love the meadows in Normandy.
The grass there is delicious. Feeding on natural pasture, Normandy cows (you can also say *"La Normande"* to impress people) are very generous: they produce extremely high-quality milk - rich in protein.
And with this milk - you guessed it - we make excellent cheeses.
Four of them can often be found on our tables:

GAME *Fill in the name of these four cheeses, their shape may well help you.*

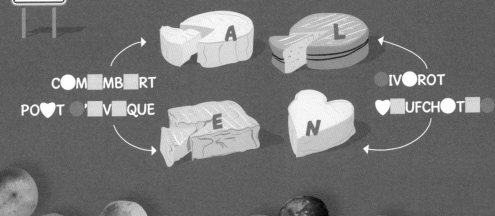

C■M■MB■RT
PO♥T ■'■V■QUE

■IV■ROT
♥■UFCH■T■■

Apples are queens in this region. There are more than 400 varieties. One of them is called the **Benedictin.**
People say it is one of the most delicious.

And do not forget that fermented apple juice is what makes **the all-famous Normandy cider.**

17

BORDEAUX

Bordeaux has for a long time owed its fortune to its port and most importantly its wine. **Because Bordeaux is also the name of the most famous vineyard in the world.** All around the city, there are thousands of hectares of vines. They are turned into wines, divided into 60 designations. Some are extremely famous: Saint-Emilion, Margaux, Pomerol, Saint-Estèphe, Pauillac, etc.

Since 2016, **a fantastic museum has opened its doors in Bordeaux: the *Cité du Vin* (City of Wine).** Designed on eight floors, this impressive place reveals all wine-making secrets in a fascinating manner. Even if you do not drink any, obviously!

GAME *What is the shortest way to reach the château?*

In Bordeaux, at Place de la Bourse, you can walk on water. Yes, it is possible! This is where the biggest water mirror in the world was created. It spreads out over 37,135 sq ft. People from Bordeaux love to come and dip their toes in when it gets hot!

Since 2007, the city of Bordeaux has been registered as a Unesco World Heritage site.

LE CANELÉ

This is Bordeaux's star cake.
Its inside is soft, it is flavoured with rum
(just a splash) and vanilla, and covered in
a caramelised crust. Tough on the outside but soft
inside. Legend has it that it was invented in the 16th century
by nuns from the Annonciade convent (the building still exists
today). One thing is certain, everyone is crazy about them!

Remember !
If you want to enjoy delicious canelés,
you have to make the batter the night before,
as it needs to rest at least 12 hours.

Ingredients
- 125 cl of milk
- 1 vanilla pod
- 125g of sugar
- 1 egg
- 60 g of flour
- 1 pinch of salt
- 25 g of butter
- 1 tbsp of rum

and some canelé moulds !

① In a saucepan, gently boil the milk and vanilla
(make sure an adult checks the pan as milk can
overflow quickly !). Leave to infuse for 5 minutes.

② In a mixing bowl, beat the sugar and egg together
then add the flour and salt, and finish with the melted butter and rum.

③ Gently pour the milk into the mixture. Mix well.
There you have it ! Now just place the bowl
in the fridge until the next day.

④ Before filling your moulds, beat the mixture
a little, then pour it into 2/3 of each mould.

2/3

⑤ In the oven for about 1 hour at 200/210°C.
Your canelés should be caramelised all over.

OYSTERS

French people love oysters.
Near Bordeaux, those bred in the area of Arcachon
are the best according to experts. A little to the North, those from
Marennes Oléron, Vendée or Cancale in Brittany also have a fantastic
reputation. Let's try to find our more about
this astonishing shellfish.

How is an oyster born?

When is the best time to eat oysters?
The best time of year to feast on delicious oysters is during the months **finishing in "-ber"**. (Septem-ber, Octo-ber, etc.)

Each oyster lays several thousand eggs that become larva.

After 20 days, these baby oysters will attach to a hard support installed in sea water.

Only a very small number of them will grow to be adults.

Once fully grown, they are removed from their support and kept for two years in breeding farms to improve their quality and size.

They are now known as "spats". These young oysters will now feed on plankton and keep growing.

In total, their breeding lasts four years!

FRENCH BASQUE COUNTRY

It is so windy over here! Our next stop is Biarritz, the European surfing capital. Surfers love the waves on the Basque coast, breaking against the city walls. And its long beach looks just like a postcard. Ideal for swimming and tanning in the sun.

 GAME *How many bull heads identical to the black one can you count among all these red scarves?*

THE BAYONNE FESTIVAL

This town becomes very lively during the summer. From the Wednesday to the first Sunday of August, the Bayonne Festival attracts thousands of visitors every year. For five days and five nights, the entire town is dressed in red and white. People also wear a red scarf around their necks and a red belt called a *cinta*. Cow races, singing, dancing, lit-up *corso* parades (float procession), *bandas* (fanfares), games for children, etc.

Such a colourful event!

21

THE PÉRIGORD
BACK TO PREHISTORIC TIMES

You can easily travel back in time when discovering the Périgord region. Back tens or even hundreds of thousands of years. This is where **most of Europe's prehistoric sites can be found.** A few explanations are in order.

In this region, the ground is made of limestone - a tender and fragile rock. Millions of years ago, the rain caused this ground to erode (wear). Lots of holes appeared. Just like in Swiss cheese. Over the millenniums, the rain water filtered in.

Naturally, caves and underground rivers started to form, as did chasms whenever the rock collapsed.

To shelter from the bad weather, **prehistoric men took refuge in these caves,** where the temperature was more pleasant. They spent their days here.

 Put the pictures back in the right order. You will discover how we traced hands (negative and positive) on the rock face.

THE VERSAILLES OF PREHISTORIC TIMES

During the 20th century, often by chance, several of these caves were discovered.

The most famous of them all? The Lascaux cave in Montignac. A cave decorated by Cro-Magnons about 20,000 years ago! Horses, stags and bulls cover all the walls. Hundreds of rock art paintings everywhere.

The cave is currently closed to preservation purposes. Luckily, you can visit its replicas (Lascaux II and Lascaux IV) that are just as good as the real thing.

GAME *What animal cannot have been painted by a Cro-Magnon man?*

With its many stalactites and stalagmites, the **PROUMEYSSAC CHASM** is nicknamed the crystal cathedral. You can go down 164 feet into the ground.

TYPICALLY
FRENCH

Good food is sacred here! Actually,
a lot of our chefs are international stars.
For example, **Paul Bocuse, Alain Ducasse**
and **Joël Robuchon** are world-renowned
French chefs.

The French gastronomic meal
is indeed registered in
humanity's heritage.

Here is a culinary tour
of our specialities.

Le foie gras
foie gras

Les escargots
snails

Les fruits de mer
seafood

La baguette de pain
French bread

Les secrets de
la cuisine
française

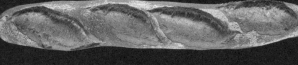

There is nothing like delicious French bread
to go with all our meals. This bread is golden
and crunchy, and baked in a long shape.
A wonderful French delight.

BREAKFAST

The first meal of the day is the most important. During the week, people have it early – between 6 and 8 am. On the menu: bread and jam, brioche, cereal or pastries. It is also nice to have a hot drink, like coffee, tea or hot chocolate, or a glass of orange juice. No doubt the best way to wake up!

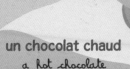

un chocolat chaud
a hot chocolate

un jus d'orange
an orange juice

des croissants
a butter croissant

des tartines de confiture
French bread with jam

Pastries & cakes

French macaroons

These round, soft cakes are made with almonds, egg whites and sugar.
You can get them in all kinds of flavours: vanilla, raspberry, chocolate, pistachio, mango, or even melon...

Chouquettes

Tarte Tatin

The Éclair

It is made with choux pastry, cooked in a long shape and filled with chocolate, vanilla or coffee cream.

The Paris-Brest

This pastry is in the shape of... a bicycle wheel! It is also made with choux pastry, but this time filled with a light praline cream. Yum!

PARIS

It is said that Paris is the capital of fashion and food, and sometimes that it is the most beautiful city in the world.
One thing is certain, Paris - our capital - is the most visited in the world.
Let's have a look around!

THE EIFFEL TOWER

1,063 feet high, 1,665 steps, 7 million visitors. Hard to imagine Paris without the Eiffel Tower.

Here is its story. In 1889, Paris organised a huge exhibition, convening all other countries to come. Each country presented its achievements or inventions. Three years earlier, a wide-scale competition was organised to elect which piece would best represent France's technical progress.
The project selected was that submitted by the engineer Gustave Eiffel (and his team): a huge iron tower anchored to the ground by four feet.
So construction began and lasted 2 years, 2 months and 5 days.

The stairs can see 30 miles around !

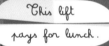

This lift pays for lunch.

The last one to reach the top start at the South pillar.

GAME

Match the bubbles to create the right sentences.

From here we has broken down

26

MONTMARTRE
THE ETERNAL VILLAGE

Now it is time to wind your way up to the Butte Montmartre (Montmartre Hill). Paris turns into a quaint village here! Believe it or not, in the 19th century, this hill was covered in gardens, vines and windmills. At the time, famous painters and poets came to live here. It is therefore no coincidence if today, on the Place du Tertre, lots of painters and cartoonists offer to draw up your portrait.

The Sacré Coeur basilica has towered over Paris since 1914. It stands out thanks to its height (272 feet!) and white colour.

Have a close look! 7 differences have slipped into these two scenes.

27

Ready for a **straight 2.5 mile walk**? Watch out for all the monuments along the way! A real parade.

3

Let's go back a few centuries. Here is the oldest monument in Paris: **the Obelisk on Place de la Concorde.** Except that it was not built here, but in Egypt, over 3,000 years ago. Then, at the beginning of the 19th century, a Frenchman called Champollion discovered the secret of the hieroglyphs. To show its appreciation, Egypt gave this large pointed column to France.

1
Everything starts at the **LOUVRE**. As you may know, it is the most visited museum in the world. Yet the Louvre was once a fortified castle, then a magnificent home to the kings of France. When admiring the *Mona Lisa* or the *Victory of Samothrace* – the museum's two stars – remember that you are standing in a former royal palace!

2
When stepping out of the Louvre, you can get some **fresh air in the TUILERIES GARDENS.** It got its name from the tile factories formerly located there, before Catherine de Medici had the Tuileries Palace built in 1564. This palace, burnt down in 1871, became the royal abode for many sovereigns.

ARC DE TRIOMPHE

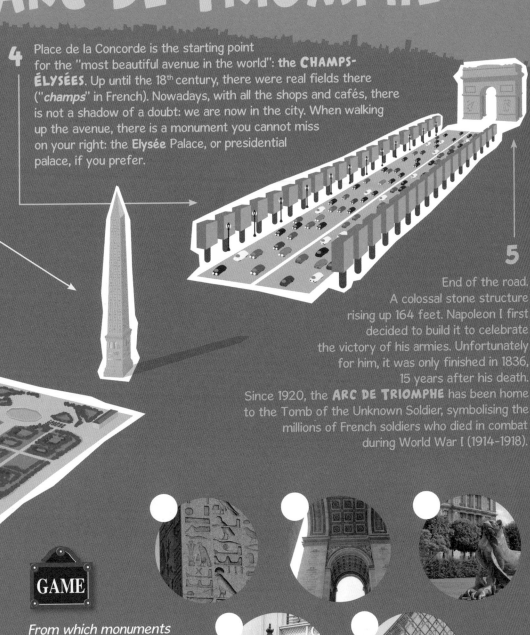

4 Place de la Concorde is the starting point for the "most beautiful avenue in the world": **the CHAMPS-ÉLYSÉES.** Up until the 18th century, there were real fields there ("*champs*" in French). Nowadays, with all the shops and cafés, there is not a shadow of a doubt: we are now in the city. When walking up the avenue, there is a monument you cannot miss on your right: the **Elysée** Palace, or presidential palace, if you prefer.

5 End of the road. A colossal stone structure rising up 164 feet. Napoleon I first decided to build it to celebrate the victory of his armies. Unfortunately for him, it was only finished in 1836, 15 years after his death. Since 1920, the **ARC DE TRIOMPHE** has been home to the Tomb of the Unknown Soldier, symbolising the millions of French soldiers who died in combat during World War I (1914-1918).

GAME

From which monuments listed on this page are these details taken?

No doubt about it, Paris is the capital of fashion. The **high fashion houses** have been set up here for a very long time now. High fashion means luxury clothing designed by great creators. They are extremely gifted. Every year and for each main season (autumn-winter and spring-summer), they design a new collection of clothes that will set the tone for future fashion. **Yves Saint-Laurent, Dior, Hermès, Jean-Paul Gaultier**, etc. These leading names in fashion make France very well-known throughout the world.

Fashion

GAME

A C E H L N O

Follow the code using the models and discover the name of a famous designer who strongly influenced the world of fashion in France.

And for all you future fashion designers! 1900, 1930, 1950, 1960, 1970, 1980, 2010
Try and match each date with the right model. You can ask your mum or dad for some help!

BIG IDEAS,
BIG SHOPS!

Paris is shopping paradise. Especially given the size of some of its shops! We have **Mr Boucicaut** to thank for that. In 1852, he had the idea of (greatly!) enlarging an old haberdashery shop, called *Bon Marché*. He had in actual fact just invented the largest shop in the world. Obviously, others wanted to follow suit. A few years later, **the Samaritaine, BHV, Printemps** and **Galeries Lafayette** opened their doors in the main Parisian boulevards.

These huge shops selling clothes, perfumes and home products still exist today. Their sumptuous decor has turned them into true monuments.

The beautiful *Galeries Lafayette* on *boulevard Haussmann*

GAME *Circle the bears that have lost their twin.*

At Christmas, the windows of these big shops are decorated in an enchanting and magical way!

31

NOTRE-DAME DE PARIS

In 1163, Maurice de Sully, the bishop of Paris, took on a huge challenge: to build the most beautiful and largest cathedral in the world for the city of Paris. **This enormous project lasted about 300 years!** Sculptors, stonemasons, carpenters and bricklayers came from all over France to work on it.

The result is quite impressive: *Notre-Dame de Paris* stands 295 feet above the ground and towers over the entire *Île de la Cité.*

A mighty fire broke out in the cathedral on 15 April 2019. Firefighters struggled for several hours against the flames and eventually managed to put out the fire. Unfortunately, most of the roof was destroyed and the 19th century spire collapsed. Naturally, a prompt decision to rebuild Notre-Dame was made. The roof frame will need to be rebuilt. This task will take several years to complete.

GAME

Notre-Dame de Paris, *is also the name of an important novel by the French writer* **Victor Hugo.** *The story revolves around the cathedral, during the 15th century. Discover the name of its two heroes.*

OVELY G · NCHBA · DA · QUAS · IPSY ES · IMOD · MERAL · THE L · O THE HU · CK

and

The palace of Versailles is located just over twelve miles away from Paris.

THE PALACE OF
VERSAILLES

Imagine yourself under the reign of **Louis XIV**. In 1660, to get away from Paris and get some peace and quiet, he asked for a palace to be built in Versailles. This was when the building became his home and that of his Court. His successors, Louis XV and Louis XVI, settled there too.

The palace is one of the most magnificent in the world: Over 720,000 sq ft, 2,000 rooms and extremely luxurious interior decor.

That is not all: the palace is surrounded with spectacular gardens. **Their creation was entrusted to André Le Nôtre, the gardener of the kings at the time.** He had green fingers for sure! The shapes are very geometrical, and follow the universal "French garden" model.
A lovely walk in Louis XIV's footsteps...

Fill in the grid to find out what Louis XIV's nickname was.

GAME

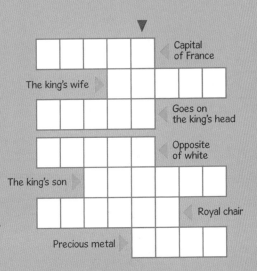

Capital of France

The king's wife

Goes on the king's head

Opposite of white

The king's son

Royal chair

Precious metal

The huge gardens as seen from the palace

LET'S SPEAK FRENCH !

Would you like to discover the French language? Here are a few vocabulary words you can use to have fun learning French... your parents will definitely be impressed!

OUI/NON
Yes/No

BONJOUR
Hello

AU REVOIR
Goodbye

S'IL VOUS PLAÎT
Please

BONSOIR
Good evening

À BIENTÔT
See you soon

PARLEZ-VOUS ANGLAIS ?
Do you speak English ?

MERCI
Thank you

1 un
2 deux
3 trois
4 quatre
5 cinq
6 six
7 sept
8 huit
9 neuf
10 dix

**Salut* !
Comment
ça va ?**

Hello, how are you?

**Bien.
Et toi ?**

Fine. And you?

*Salut
*is used at any
moment of the day,
kind of like Hi.*

**Où sont
les toilettes ?**

Where are the restrooms?

BLEU BLANC ROUGE

blue　　　white　　　red

Comment t'appelles-tu ?

What is your name?

Je m'appelle *Martin*.

My name is Martin.

Quel âge as-tu ?

How old are you?

J'ai dix ans.

I am ten.

Jules and I thought about
our favourite places in France.
To each their own.
Here is the result!

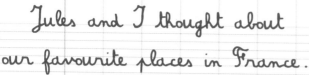

Discover the salt marshes
and rice paddies in the Camargue
area, among the horses...

Enjoy the dozens of theatre shows
during the Festival
of Avignon in July.

See
life in pink
down in
Toulouse.

Glide along the "Green Venice" canals
in Poitiers' marshes.

Cycle
all around
the île de Ré
island.

and flamingoes!

10/10
for the Calissons
treats from
Aix-en-Provence.

Cheer on the cyclists
DURING THE TOUR
DE FRANCE in July

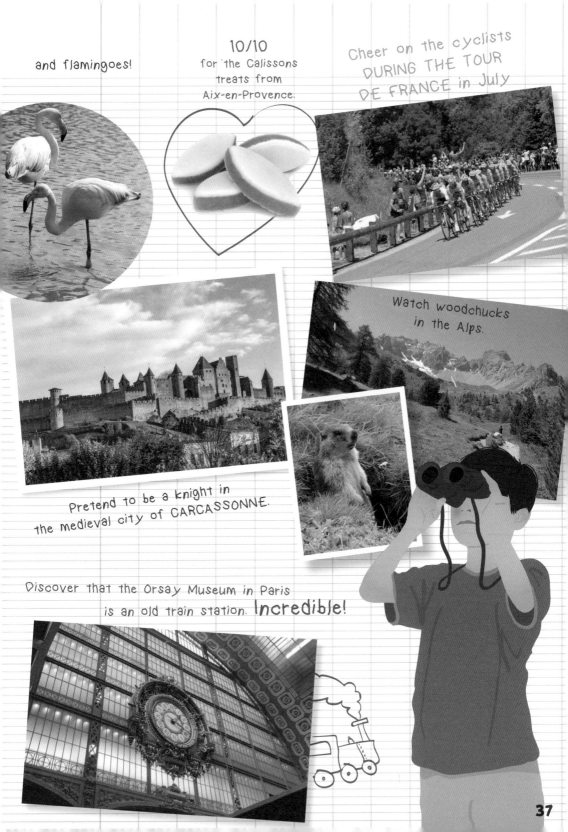

Watch woodchucks
in the Alps.

Pretend to be a knight in
the medieval city of CARCASSONNE.

Discover that the Orsay Museum in Paris
is an old train station. Incredible!

THE CÔTE D'AZUR

Set between the sea and mountains, the Côte d'Azur's landscapes are really worth a visit. **All the towns are luxurious down there**: luxury hotels, gastronomic restaurants, chic cafés, etc. Most importantly it is where all the stars go! Lots of celebrities live along the Côte d'Azur, or go and spend their summer holidays there.
Above all, they love the sun and beaches in Saint-Tropez!

GAME

The bubbles from this scene have been mixed up. Give each character the right speech bubble.

When you come to the Côte d'Azur, the city of Nice is a must-see, as is **the Promenade des Anglais. This avenue, lined with palm trees and stretching out over almost 4.5 miles,** owes its name to British aristocrats. As of the 19th century, they declared Nice to be their favourite place to holiday during the winter.

When you wander around the old part of Nice, with its lively streets and colourful buildings, it looks more like Italy. How nice!

CANNES FILM FESTIVAL

Lights, camera... Action! The Cannes Film Festival is held on the Côte d'Azur in May every year. Devoted to cinema, it is no doubt the most important in the world. And I am not just saying that because we are French.

It was created in 1946, and rewards the best artists every year: directors, actors, actresses. Still today, the most sought-after reward is the *Palme d'Or*. The official jury awards it to the best film. Why that name (Golden Palm)? Simply because the trophy is shaped like a palm leaf in reference to the palm trees along *La Croisette* - the boulevard that runs along the sea in Cannes.

 GAME *Have you heard of this English director, who won the Palme d'Or twice? Blacken out the words in the list to discover his name using the remaining letters.*
CLOSE-UP · CREDITS · DIRECTOR · DRAMA · DUB · FOCUS · MOVIE · SCREEN · SETS · SHOT · TRAILER · ZOOM

C L O S E U P K D
E N S E T S I
T C R E D I T S R
R S H O T L E
A O F D R A M A C
I O A D U B T
L C C M O V I E O
E U Z O O M R
R H S S C R E E N

MARSEILLE

Stop-over in France's oldest town: Marseille.
It was founded over 2,600 years ago by Greek seamen from Phocaea.
This is why it is sometimes nicknamed The Phocaean city.

If you come to Marseille, you will no doubt come across the Old Port.
As the old fishing and trade port, it is the city's most prevalent place.

If you lift your head a little, you can admire - at the top of the hill - the **Notre-Dame-de-la-Garde** basilica. Perched at the top is the "*Bonne Mère*" (Good Mother): a golden statue of the Virgin Mary looking over the fishermen and citizens since 1864.

The "Bonne mère"

GAME

This fish-based soup is very well-known in Marseille.
It used to be a fisherman's dish. Do you know what it is called?

U A B E I L O S

40

LES BAUX-DE-PROVENCE

Here is one of the most beautiful villages in Provence. And one of the most visited. Gripped to the side of a huge cliff, it looks out over Arles and Les Arpilles - a small mountain range. **Such a breathtaking viewpoint!** At its far end, the village opens out onto a fortress taking you back to the Middle Ages.

Torn down during the 12th century by Catalan enemies, the castle was rebuilt during the 13th century by the lords of Baux. From then on, everything was done to ensure good defence: dungeon, watchtower, deep moat to prevent access to the castle, etc. Intruders, beware!

GAME

*You will discover reconstructed Middle Age machines up at the castle in Les Baux-de-Provence. The most impressive is a 52-foot catapult. It could **project stone balls weighing 50 to 100 kg, up to 220 yards away.***

To find out the name of this catapult, put the launch stages back in the right order.

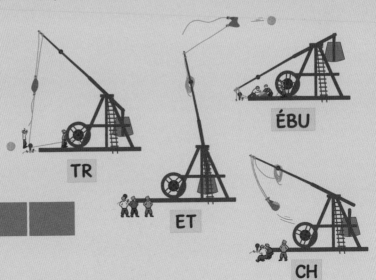

TR

ET

ÉBU

CH

41

SOUTHERN SCENTS!

THYME, BAY LAUREL, ROSEMARY, ETC.

The vegetation in Provence's hillsides is known as **garrigue**. It is made up of large bushes, shrubs and most importantly aromatic plants that make you want to cook. These many herbs, with their delicious scents, bring a touch of sunshine to dishes and sauces.

LAVENDER

In the Vaucluse and Haute-Provence regions, this purple-flowered plant grows as far as the eye can see. Pure delight for the eyes... and nose. **Lavender gives off a delicious scent.** The most refined type (and also the most expensive) is fine lavender - which is actually used for making perfume.

GAME

Discover the name of a speciality with many different scents, which you can taste in Provence.

To do so, cross out the herbs in the steam.

SOUP

THE OLIVE:
THE QUEEN OF PROVENCE

Just like everywhere else around the Mediterranean, olive trees grow well in Provence.
So well in fact that they can live for hundreds of years. The hot and dry climate in this region is ideal for the fruit growing on these trees: olives. **Green in September, black in December**- once the olives have been crushed and pressed, delicious olive oil can be made.

PERFUME FROM GRASSE

With its warm and sunny climate, the city of Grasse has **the perfect soil for growing flowers.**
It has long been renowned for its roses, orange blossom and jasmine. Over time, Grasse became the world perfume capital.

Thyme
Laurel
Tarragon
Chive
Parsley
Dill
Olive
Rosemary

THYME
LAUREL
PIGON
TARRA CHIVE
SILL
DRILEY
PARS TOARY
O ROSEMU
OLIVE

WHAT YOU WILL NEED:

3 eggs

200 g of flour

1/2 packet of backing powder

12 cl of crème fraîche

2 tbsp of pistou sauce

2 tbsp of tomato paste

2 tbsp of chopped black olives

2 tbsp of olive oil

80 g of grated Emmental cheese

1 Mix the flour in with the baking powder in a large bowl. Add the beaten eggs along with the crème fraîche and olive oil, then sprinkle the grated Emmental cheese in.

2 Separate the batter into three portions. Add the tomato paste, pistou and black olives to each of them. Mix in well.

3 Pour all 3 preparations into a greased mould, starting with the black olive one, and finishing with the tomato one.

4 Ask an adult to put it in the oven at 180°C (th. 6) for 45 minutes.

SOUTHERN PAINTERS

The light is so beautiful here! Ideal for our photos. Now I understand better why many painters drew their inspiration from the South of France. The best example of this is in **Paul Cézanne**'s paintings. This impressionist* painter was born in Aix-en-Provence in 1839. He loved painting his favourite model: **the Sainte-Victoire mountain,** that towered over his home town.

* see p.16

The light in the South attracted lots of painters at the time. **Vincent Van Gogh**, for example, came to Arles in 1888. He completed a series of paintings known throughout the world: **Sunflowers.**

Vase with fifteen sunflowers - Arles 1889
Van Gogh Museum - Amsterdam

Later on, the area also attracted **Henri Matisse**. He was the leader of fauvism: he loved to paint with bright and highly original colours.
At the time, his paintings were outrageous!
In 1921, he settled down in Nice to find some new inspiration. To find out more, head to the Matisse Museum. It makes for a lovely visit!

Will you have as much inspiration as Matisse when colouring this **Cat with goldfish***?*

PÉTANQUE

This game of boules is particularly popular in Provence. **You often see people playing it in village squares.** It was born near Marseille in the early 20th century. At first, players used to call it "the long one" or "the Provençal game".

They had to run three steps before throwing their ball. The game changed in 1907: a new way of playing was imposed, with no run-up so the players' feet had to stay grounded. **In 1910, the game of _Pétanque_ was officially created!** It has come a long way since then.

Well Cesar, is it our win?

the jack ball

GAME

To score a point, your ball must be closest to the **jack ball** (cochonnet in French).
A team can score several points if they have two or more balls better positioned than those of the opposing team. Sometimes, very precise measurements need to be made.

TEAM A   TEAM B

Which team wins the round, and how many points will it score?

You can cut this ruler out to measure the distance between the balls and jack ball.

45

ON ROMANS TRACKS

Stop-over in Nîmes. No doubt about it, the **Romans were here.**
They arrived in the 2nd century B.C. and covered the town in sumptuous buildings. Let's explore three of the most famous ones.

THE AMPHITHEATRE

The best-preserved one from Roman times. It dates back to the 1st century. **This circular monument welcomed gladiator or animal fights in front of 20,000 spectators.** Nowadays, concerts and sporting competitions are held there.

THE MAISON CARRÉE (SQUARE HOUSE IN FRENCH)

It is not really square, as it measures 86 feet long and 50 feet wide. However, at the time of its construction (1st century), when Nîmes was known as *Nemausus*, the word 'rectangle' did not exist. In any case, **this temple - dedicated to the son and grandson of Emperor August -** is the only one dating back to Antiquity that has been fully preserved!

THE PONT DU GARD

Watch out, this is a real masterpiece. The Romans really were an incredible people. Built towards year 50 just a few miles away from Nîmes, **the Pont du Gard was in fact an aqueduct bridge.** This means its purpose was to carry water from one place to another. Thanks to its airborne channel the bridge was able to cross the Gard river and provide for the entire city of Nîmes.

 Find the 7 pictures that have nothing at all to do with Roman times!

THE GIANTS FROM AUVERGNE

The most recent, all part of the Puys chain, were formed 100,000 years before our time, and were **still spitting lava just 7,000 years ago.** Who are they? The volcanoes in Auvergne. There are about 200 of them, and they form **the largest volcanic park in Europe.** They are currently dormant, but they could still wake up. Rest assured, it would not be any time soon.

Our Earth:

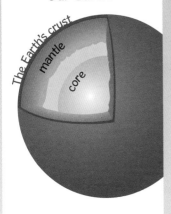

The crust is made of huge plates that move slowly because of the mantle's rocks also moving.

Sometimes, these plates spread out or overlap, **this is called plate tectonics.**

Everything started **60 million years ago** when the Eurasian plate met the African plate and slid under it (forming the Alps.) The Eurasian plate then stretched out, became thinner and cracked. Rifts started to appear in the Massif Central area (Auvergne region).

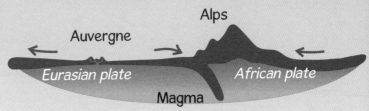

Now thinner, the Earth's crust put less pressure on the mantle. As a result, the mantle's rocks melted in some places, leading to the creation of magma. The magma then rose up to the surface through the plate's rifts. **This is what formed the very first volcanoes in Auvergne.**

LYON

Lyon is known for having been the capital of Gaul - the old name for France. That was during Roman times. Then, the city was called *Lugdunum*. Later on, print works and silk manufacture gave this fascinating city its reputation. And there is more.

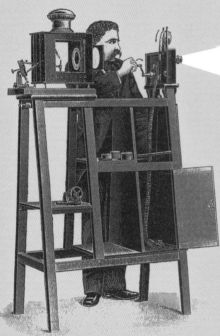

Le cinématographe Lumière: projection.

THANK YOU FOR THE INVENTION

In 1895, two brothers from Lyon, **Auguste and Louis Lumière**, had a genius idea. They put together a machine capable of recording movement, meaning they could film. It became known as a **cinematograph**. This fantastic machine could also project animated images on a big screen. So, as you have no doubt guessed, Lyon was where cinema was invented.

If you come here, why not visit the **Lumière Institute.** Set in the old family home, you can learn everything there is to know about what the Lumière brothers discovered.

THE FÊTE DES LUMIÈRES (LIGHT FESTIVAL)

A great time to visit Lyon? Probably around the 8th of December. Every year, for four nights, all the city's buildings, monuments and gardens are lit up in the most stunning way. It is truly amazing. Lyon deserves its nickname: *Ville Lumière* (Light City).

BON APPÉTIT!

In Lyon, people love to eat. Really love it.
It has always been like that. You could actually
describe the city as the capital of gastronomy.

If you go to a *bouchon*, which is a typical Lyon
restaurant, you had better be hungry.
You can eat some very filling specialities there!

GAME *Find out what
these funny
dish names
correspond to.*

CHEESE OF HEAD
Pork that has been cooked
and seasoned with
carrots, shallots,
pickles, etc.

JESUS FROM LYON
A dried sausage.

APRON OF SAPPER
Speciality made from
cow's stomach.

LET US SCRAPE !
Pork, duck
or chicken fat.

Foies de volaille
Fromage de tête
Grattons
Jésus de Lyon
Saucisson brioché
Gras double
Tablier de sapeur
Cardons à la möelle
Quenelles Nantua
~
Cervelle de canut
~
Bugnes, Coussins

FANCY A BIT OF CHEESE?

As you have no doubt heard, the French really love their cheese. **There are over 1,200 different kinds from all over France.** Made with cow, goat or sheep's milk, they can be round or triangular, firm or creamy, white or orangey - there is something for everyone. Depending on the region, climate and pasture land, their taste varies greatly. Let's go and discover some of these famous cheeses.

GAME

Cow, goat or sheep's milk? Follow the red line to find out which animal each cheese comes from.

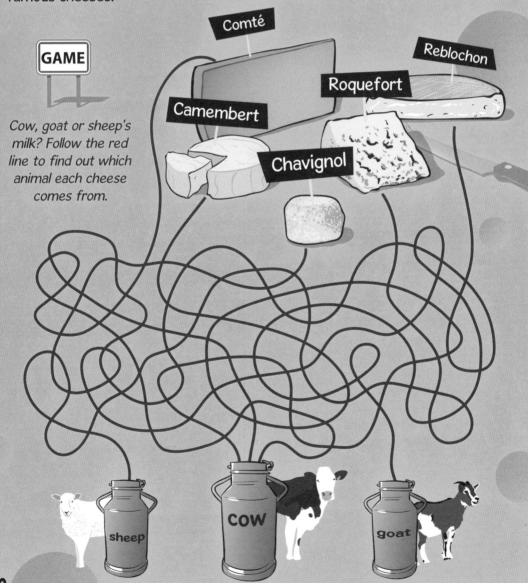

THE MONT BLANC

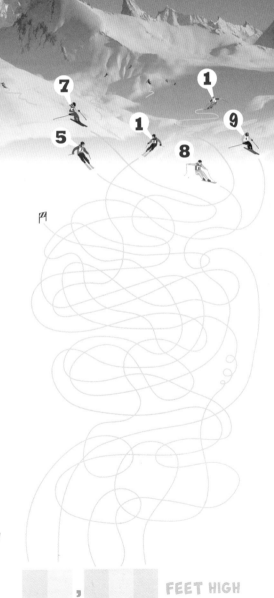

7 **1**

5 **1** **9**

8

Thrilling sensations up ahead!
The Mont Blanc is the highest mountain peak in France, as well as in Europe. It towers proudly over the Alps - a mountain chain formed 60 million years ago *(see page 47).*

Nowadays, every year, thousands of Alpinists try to climb it.

Without forgetting the many holiday-makers who come and ski down this huge mountain. In fact, did you know that skiing came from Norway and has existed in the Alps since the 1880's?

GAME

Follow the trajectory for each skier, and note down on the podium the winners' numbers. This will tell you how high the Mont Blanc is.

, FEET HIGH

WELCOME TO THE ALSACE!

The Alsace is a very special French region. **Indeed, it was successively French then German, then French again for good in 1945.** Having changed nationality so many times, people living in the Alsace grew attached to their own language, a dialect quite similar to German.

It always feels great to come back here. Sometimes you even feel like you are back in the past... The half-timbered houses in towns and villages such as Strasbourg, Colmar and Kayserberg take you back to the Middle Ages.

Towards the end of the year, the main town squares turn into **magical Christmas markets**. And when the cold sets in, why not try some local specialities: the *flammeküeche* (grilled tart covered in bacon bits and cream) and another dish that you can guess the name of below.

GAME *Discover the name of this special Alsace dish.*

3 times in "sausages"

Same as the second-to-last letter

End of "dinner"

Twice in "knack"

Like the 2nd letter

In the middle of "yum"

3 times in "Alsacian"

Appears in "French" and "meal"

The end of "hunger"

Twice in "tasty"

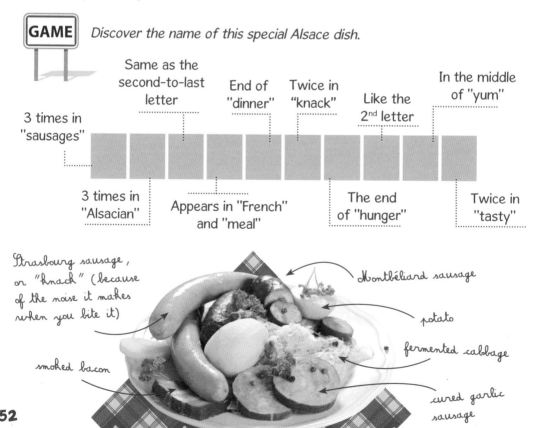

Strasbourg sausage, or "knack" (because of the noise it makes when you bite it)

Montbéliard sausage

potato

fermented cabbage

smoked bacon

cured garlic sausage

52

REIMS:
THE LAND OF THE KINGS

Reims cathedral stands with great pride. Built from 1211, **Notre-Dame** (that is its name) is still a masterpiece of Gothic-style architecture. People say its front face is of exceptional beauty.

It is also the cathedral of the Kings of France: 25 of them, from Louis VIII to Charles X, were crowned there. The sovereigns used to be crowned here in memory of **Clovis**, considered to be the **first King of France**. He was christened in Reims in 498.

Reims cathedral is listed as a Unesco World Heritage site.

Discover this stained-glass window in Notre-Dame cathedral using the number/colour code.

POP SOME CHAMPAGNE OPEN!

Champagne is a kind of sparkling wine known throughout the world. It contributes to France's pride and reputation. It is produced in... the historical Champagne area, located right near Reims.

BELFRIES
THE PEOPLE'S TOWERS

If you can make out their pretty silhouettes in the landscape, that means you have arrived in the North of France.

Built from the Middle Ages, belfries were in fact communal towers. **Their purpose was to show the town's power and independence. They symbolised the people's power in the face of the Church or lords and their dungeons.** Belfries were also used as bell and watch towers. Over time, they became places to have parties and gatherings. Nowadays, they can be visited.

In the Hauts-de-France region, 23 belfries are classified as Unesco World Heritage sites. Among them: Armentières, Arras, Calais, Dunkirk, etc. The one in Lille, rising up 341 feet, is the highest in Northern Europe.

GAME

Measure how high these 3 belfries are.

340 feet high

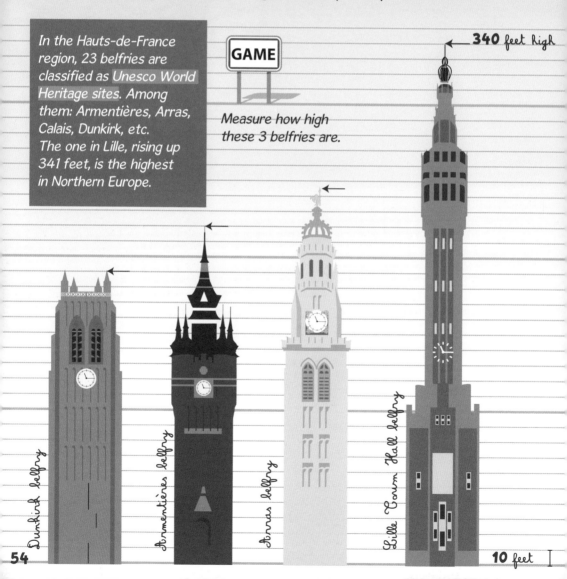

Dunkirk belfry

Armentières belfry

Arras belfry

Lille Town Hall belfry

10 feet

LILLE

Over 15,000 sellers, 2 million visitors and tonnes of great deals: objects, antiquities, games, toys, books, etc.

Every year, during the first week-end of September, the city of Lille organises the biggest jumble sale in Europe. It actually turns into a huge market and car boot sale.
This event dates back to 1127!
If you have some pocket money, this is a great place to spend it!
You can also make the most of it to taste some famous *"moules-frites"* (mussels and chips).
They are a tradition here.

The old part of Lille and its sculpted and colourful buildings are also a must-see. The combination of bricks and stone is amazing.

How many people came to the jumble sale with at least one bag?

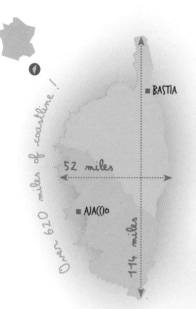

■ BASTIA

52 miles

■ AJACCIO

114 miles

Over 620 miles of coastline!

CORSICA

Heading to paradise!
Corsica will no doubt dazzle you.
And not just with its sunny weather.
Mountains, canyons, beaches, forests,
everything is stunning there. Corsica deserves
its nickname: the Island of Beauty.

BY THE SEA

Beautiful beaches, enchanting coves,
transparent sea. Obviously, we would go to Corsica
on holiday every year if we could. It feels like you
are in paradise. And it is always so sunny.
In fact it beats everywhere else in France.
The place we loved most: Bonifacio.
This town is perched on the top of huge cliffs.
From here, we can go on excursions to the famous
calanques and sea caves.

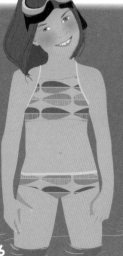

E H I L O R S T V Y

56

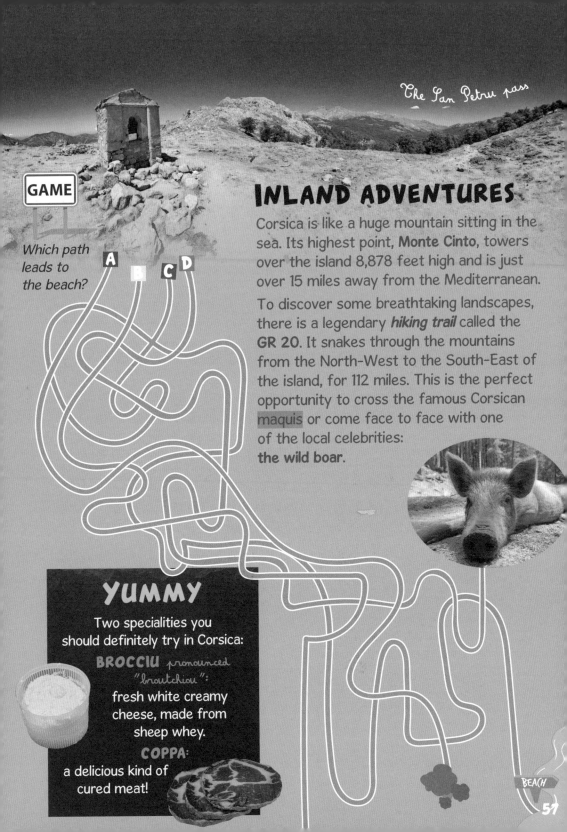

The San Petru pass

GAME

Which path leads to the beach?

A B C D

INLAND ADVENTURES

Corsica is like a huge mountain sitting in the sea. Its highest point, **Monte Cinto**, towers over the island 8,878 feet high and is just over 15 miles away from the Mediterranean.

To discover some breathtaking landscapes, there is a legendary *hiking trail* called the **GR 20**. It snakes through the mountains from the North-West to the South-East of the island, for 112 miles. This is the perfect opportunity to cross the famous Corsican maquis or come face to face with one of the local celebrities: the wild boar.

YUMMY

Two specialities you should definitely try in Corsica:

BROCCIU pronounced "*broutchiou*": fresh white creamy cheese, made from sheep whey.

COPPA: a delicious kind of cured meat!

BEACH

55

THE FANTASTIC FRENCH

They give France its reputation and have incredible talent; let's meet a few French celebrities.

EDITH PIAF
Singer and lyricist
1915-1963

GÉRARD DEPARDIEU
Actor
born in 1948

MOLIÈRE
Actor and playwright
1622-1673

CHARLES DE GAULLE
Army General and politician
1890-1970

ZINÉDINE ZIDANE
Footballer and coach
born in 1972

Link each accessory with its correct owner, then put the right label on them.

GAME

THE GLOSSARY

Allied Forces
The countries opposed to Nazi Germany, Italy and Japan during World War II. Some of these countries were: the United States, the Soviet Union and the United Kingdom.

Designation
How a product is named according to its origin, its place of manufacture.

Archangel
Angel of a higher ranking.

Calanques
Small coves surrounded by very high rocks.

Catalan
People living in Catalonia. Catalonia is in the North-East of Spain.

Convent
The place where monks and nuns live. It can also be called a monastery.

Dialect
A special form of language, specific to a certain region.

Fauvism
Painting style from the early 20th century, characterised by the use of bright colours in contrast with one another.

Fermentation
When sugar turns into alcohol, as caused by germs if there is no oxygen.

Spire
Pyramid- or cone-shaped cover on top of a bell tower or standard tower.

Gothic-style
Gothic architecture was very common between the 12th and 16th centuries, especially for the construction of cathedrals. It is characterised by its pretty vaults and large windows.

Haberdashery
A shop specialised in sewing, thread and buttons.

Hieroglyphs
Type of writing used by the Egyptians at the time of ancient Pharaohs. They represented small images or symbols.

Lava
The melted rock produced by an erupting volcano.

Maquis
A thick landscape of small trees and shrubs.

Megalith
A very large stone monument, such as a dolmen or menhir.

Unesco World Heritage site
Unesco (United Nations Educational, Scientific and Cultural Organization) has established a list of 1,000 cultural or natural sites it considers should be either known or protected, that have great importance on an international level. In France for instance, the Mont-Saint-Michel and the palace of Versailles are included in this list.

Pilgrim
A believer who travels to a sacred place relating to his/her religion. For instance Mecca for Muslims or Rome for Christians.

Pictorial
Relating to painting when it is considered as an art.

Plankton
Tiny animals or plants that live in the sea.

Rock art
Rock art painting is done on a wall.

Maquis in the Provence area

ANSWERS

Page 6:

Page 18:

Page 9:
The record (2017) is **74** days, **3** hours **35** minutes and **46** seconds.

Page 10:
cormorant: 8
Northern gannet: 12
puffin: 8

Page 11:
OUESSANT

Page 12: We can make 8 more.

Page 13:

Page 14:
8 x 10 = 80
80 x 2 = 160
160 + 40 = 200
200 x 2 = 400
400 + 112 = **512 ft**

Page 16:
Les Nymphéas
(Water Lilies)

Page 17:

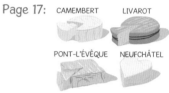
CAMEMBERT   LIVAROT
PONT-L'ÉVÊQUE   NEUFCHÂTEL

Page 21:
There are 7.

Page 22:

Page 23:
Cro-Magnon never crossed paths with the dinosaurs!

Page 26:
- From here we can see 30 miles around!
- The stairs start at the South pillar.
- The last one to reach the top pays for lunch.
- This lift has broken down.

Page 27:

Page 29:

Page 30:
Coco Chanel

1900   1930   1950   1960

1970   1980   2010

Page 31:

Page 32:
THE LOVELY GIPSY ESMERALDA and QUASIMODO THE HUNCHBACK

Page 33: the SUN KING

P	A	R	I	S			◀ Capital of France

The king's wife ▶ Q U E E N

C R O W N ◀ Goes on the king's head

B L A C K ◀ Opposite of white

The king's son ▶ P R I N C E

T H R O N E ◀ Royal chair

Precious metal ▶ G O L D

Page 38:

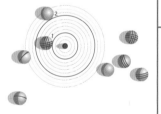

Get down from that chair!

Woof

Dad, look at that huge boat!

Lucien, would you like a biscuit?

No, someone must have forgotten it.

Is this cardigan yours?

Page 39: Ken Loach

Page 40: Bouillabaisse

Page 41: This catapult is called a TREBUCHET.

Page 42: PISTOU soup

Page 45:
Team A scores 2 points.

Page 46:

Page 50:

SHEEP > Roquefort

COW > Camembert
Comté
Reblochon

GOAT > Chavignol

Page 52: SAUERKRAUT

Page 51:
Mont Blanc peak: 15,781 ft high

Page 54:
- Dunkerque Belfry: 190 feet
- Armentières Belfry: 220 feet
- Arras Belfry: 245 feet

Page 55:
There are **16 people** with a bag, including me!

Page 56:
- It's lovely here.

Page 57:
Path **C** leads to the beach.

Page 58:

CHARLES DE GAULLE

GÉRARD DEPARDIEU

MOLIÈRE

ZINÉDINE ZIDANE

ÉDITH PIAF

In the same collection:
PARIS FOR KIDS
NORMANDY FOR KIDS
THE LOIRE VALLEY
CHÂTEAUX

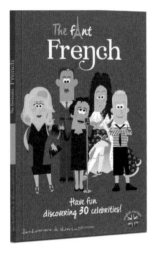

By the same author:
THE FANTASTIC FRENCH

30 celebrities to discover in a fun way!

They are actors, athletes, writers, inventors or presidents.
They give France its reputation. Everyone should know who they are.
They are all in this new children's book.

From Chanel to Voltaire, Victor Hugo, Edith Piaf, Claude Monet or Gustave Eiffel, this book encourages young readers to learn about 30 celebrities.

Authors: Stéphanie and Hugues Bioret, Julie Godefroy
Illustrations: Julie Godefroy et Stéphanie Bioret

Acknowledgements: Guy Bioret - Mémorial de Caen - Les Machines de l'Île, SPL Le Voyage à Nantes - Fondation Claude Monet, Giverny

Photo credits: Hugues Bioret ; Bernard Boué ; Julie Godefroy ; Ghislaine Godefroy ; © Adobe Stock ; © Wikipédia ; © Pixabay

© Éditions Bonhomme de Chemin, 2015/Copyright

CONTACT:
tel. +33 (0)6 13 54 19 80
bonhommedechemin@orange.fr
www.bonhommedechemin.fr

In compliance with law no.49956 from 16 July 1949
regarding publications for children

ISBN : 979-10-92714-24-1

Raynaud Imprimeur (79) printing company, France
Printed on PEFC paper
Printing completed in march 2023
Legal submission: october 2017

PEFC
10-31-1336